BOOK DESCRIPTION

We cannot continue to educate our children for a world that no longer exists. A glance at any employment website shows a list of job titles unheard of 20 years ago. All of them require some form of lateral thinking as the focus has shifted from mechanical processes to creative solutions. We need to train our brains to break free of habitual, conditioned thought patterns.

The puzzles in this book will gradually guide the reader to start seeing information as something to be processed rather than memorized. As we learn to evaluate the facts given critically, we can work out how to fit them together in unexpected ways to achieve different outcomes. We can also improve our ability to communicate our ideas while considering other points of view.

Paul D. Pantera is an entrepreneur and US Navy Sailor Senior Enlisted Leader who has trained hundreds of Junior Sailors over his 16+ year career. His goal is to provide parents, educators, and young adults with the tools to bridge the gap between their children's education and the skills they require in the real world. One of the biggest challenges is problem-solving abilities. He has put together a practical approach to create a basic system to develop a different way of thinking. The Pantheria Life Tools are games, journals, and books with the simple goal of building productive citizens.

LATERAL THINKING LESSONS AND PUZZLES TO UNLOCK CREATIVITY AND LEADERSHIP ABILITY

Simple and Easy Methods to Boost Brain Power in Ages 16 and Up

Paul D. Pantera

Panterax Ltd

ISBN 978-1-957442-10-5

Additional Books in the Pantheria Series:

Puzzle Books

Pantheria Ultimate Puzzle Book: Over 70 Choice
Puzzles for Adults – ISBN 978-1-957442-00-6

Pantheria Grand Book of 200 Grid Logic, Sudoku,
Codeword, & Word Search Puzzles for Adults:
A Mega-Collection of Grid Logic, Sudoku, Codewords
and Wordsearches! – ISBN 978-1-957442-08-2

Journals

Pantheria Life Log Journal (Black) - 978-1-957442-01-3

Coming Soon

Military Grade Adulting: What everyone expects
you to already know about Goal setting, Financial
Planning, Career Development, and Keeping your
life together.

DEDICATION

This book was inspired by the many smart and savvy young people that have filled my life with purpose and commitment; first and foremost, my children and grandchildren Jelani, Reuben, Casie, Eli, and Mila to whom I hold deep love, great pride, and respect. My friends whom I hold in my heart as my children Paola, Jesus, and Asael Mancillas. My friend and shipmate Joshua Smalls as well as the thousands of shipmates I've served with onboard the USS Wayne E. Meyer (DDG 108), USS Spruance (DDG 111), and White Sands Missile Range. May this book help open the minds of many now and forever.

THANKS

I am eternally grateful to my wife, Yolanda, for her constant love and support. I also want to thank the team that spent hours of hard work to help put this book together: Alli Marks, Briar Smith, and Athina Leonti.

TABLE OF CONTENTS

INTRODUCTION

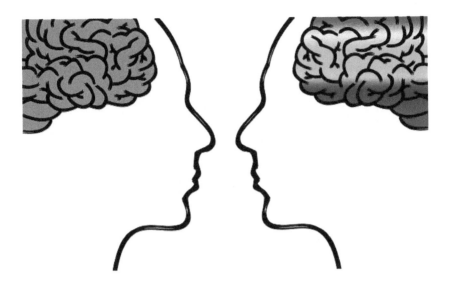

One of the magical things that makes riddles, puzzles, and brainteasers so much fun is their element of surprise. They often force us to set aside our usual way of thinking so that we can find creative loopholes to reach unexpected conclusions. I love seeing the facepalm moment when my trainees follow the sometimes illogical thought process to find a solution. The best part of interacting with young people in this context is following their arguments in favor of a solution I had not considered.

This is the key to lateral thinking. It involves analyzing all raw data from different perspectives to see connections that may not be clear at first glance. This creates a deeper understanding of the issues, making it easier to develop unique solutions to suit specific situations. This process is essential to business strategy within individual organizations and their clients in the 21st-century workplace. Many multinational corporations include some brainteasers or problem-solving tests as part of their interview process.

Lateral thinking can sometimes seem to be following a gut feeling, especially when you have to adopt a creative, innovative and out-of-the-box approach to consider aspects of the situation that may not be factual or logical. But, ultimately, with practice, you will develop the ability to find patterns where there seems to be none to arrive at either a correct answer or at least an alternative to an existing one.

The puzzles in this book may initially seem impossible because you will be given very little information about each scenario that you are expected to resolve. However, it will always be enough to reach a conclusion that you can support. Your solutions may not always match the ones provided at the end of each chapter.

Your aim is not to find "the right" solution. The real challenge is to question the way you think about thinking. Let go of what you thought you knew about problem-solving and figure out how to embrace your creativity.

Removing the faults in a stage-coach may produce a perfect stage-coach, but it is unlikely to produce the first motor car.
Edward de Bono

The Benefits of Lateral Thinking

1. Lateral thinking is about using all the information about a situation to find the most efficient response instead of simply identifying problems to find a quick fix.

2. It inspires creativity to discover unique solutions to specific situations rather than following boring, formulaic patterns.

3. It boosts productivity by eliminating unnecessarily tedious processes. This avoids boredom and motivates people to keep working.

4. Looking at alternatives together can also improve the quality of teamwork by inspiring individuals to build on

each other's ideas together instead of competing to find the solution.

5. Lateral thinking is a crucial skill set in leadership. People below you in the chain of command will immediately see that you inspire them to work smart instead of hard and will be more willing to work hard when it is necessary. People above you in the command chain will see the results of your innovative thinking in your team's work.

Another significant advantage of lateral thinking is that it changes how we view our effort's outcomes.

Dealing with Failure

We don't make mistakes, just happy little accidents.
-Bob Ross

The painter, educator, and PBS presenter, Bob Ross said: It is easy to see how this makes sense from an artistic perspective. Every attempt to paint, draw or write, even if the end product is horrible and you would never show a soul, offers practice for your craft to increase your skills and make your next attempt more successful. Sometimes, it takes a new perspective to turn a failure into a success. History is riddled with innovation that came directly from failure.

The Rocket Chemical Company employee Norman Larsen worked long and hard on a formula to prevent corrosion, which is done by displacing water. In his logbook, he labeled each attempt "Water Displacement," followed by the number of attempts he had made. Can you use your experience in lateral thinking to see where this story is going? After 39 failed attempts, he finally created a formula that was so successful the company changed its name to the now-famous WD-40 based on the description, Water Displacement 40th attempt. It was initially used to protect the Atlas rocket from rust. However, what made it a household name was packaging it in aerosol cans that made it suitable for residential use.

You are almost certainly familiar with a different case in which millions of lives were saved as a result of a scientist re-examining what he thought was a failure. Alexander Flemming was a physician and microbiologist whose job was researching the staphylococci bacteria. Flemming was known for his untidy lab space, and before a family vacation, he had stacked the Petri dishes with the bacteria cultures in the corner of his desk. When he returned a few weeks later, he had discovered that mold had contaminated one of the Petri dishes. As he was throwing the contaminated dish away, he realized that the mold had dissolved the bacteria. From there, he began to research the mold and its antibacterial powers. This was the discovery of penicillin, and since then, it has saved the lives of over 200 million people–something to bring up if someone accuses you of having a messy workspace.

The point is that failure is in the eye of the beholder. Spencer Silver was a scientist working on creating a new glue to use on 3M adhesive tape. In the process, he accidentally made a weaker glue that was pressure-sensitive. He tried unsuccessfully for years to market this new glue, including an idea to use it as a spray-on adhesive for notice boards. Finally, a colleague of his, Arthur Fry, thought it would be perfect for attaching his bookmark to his hymn book. 3M initially called it the "Press and Peel." The idea appeared so far-fetched that it only took off when 3M gave it away as free samples.

These stories show us that failure doesn't have to mean the end. It would be unrealistic to expect every idea to be a huge success. What we can do is change our definition of and attitude to failure. We have been taught to think of failure as the opposite of success. We often start off hoping that an idea will fix a problem precisely the way we said it would. We become attached to our ideas and see them as a reflection of our abilities or thought processes. A common reaction to failure is, "I am such an idiot!" Then we have to deal with the emotions that come with that attitude. In the process, we may even give up on finding the formula for a substance that could dispel water to prevent rust. Can you imagine if Norman had given up on the water displacement idea after the first try, or even the thirtieth?

You have had a lot of practice challenging the way you have been taught to think. So, let's look at different ways of dealing with what we perceive as failure.

The first step is to accept that an idea didn't work as you presented it, or more accurately, as you expected. This is easier to do if you don't become too attached to achieving a specific outcome immediately. Instead, try to think of your efforts as a way to understand the problem instead of just a quick fix, "right" answer. Sometimes you will understand the problem so quickly that your first solution will be a perfect fit. Other times you may need more clues or even get some help from other people.

The sooner you accept this, the easier it will be to tweak ideas, adjust the fit and try again. It will also help ease the emotions you feel when you define failure as something permanent.

When you can see failure as a stepping stone to success, the following steps will come more naturally:

1. Do not wallow in the emotions you have been taught to associate with failure
2. Analyze the problem
3. Look objectively at what worked and what didn't.
4. Try again

First, you must accept that the idea did not work out as you thought it would. Accept the feelings that failure has brought. Nobody likes to fail; it often hurts. Accepting that reality will help get past the pain.

Those negative feelings that accompany failure can, if allowed to fester, diminish your willingness to try again, don't let them! The only actual failure is when you give up. Understand the emotions that surround your failure and remember that they are temporary. You will recover and try again.

When you have processed your emotions and a clear head has prevailed, try and find the reason for the failure. Be as honest with yourself in this step as you can. For example, maybe your product failed because the people were not ready for your genius idea, but you will only know if that is true at a much later date. Even if that is the conclusion of your analysis, the way forward to this is to make the product something people are ready for or market so that people realize the power of your product.

Evaluate the idea. No solution is ever a complete failure. Here is where you shift your perspective from thinking that you created a failure to understanding, as Bob Ross would say, a happy accident. Try to find the positive aspects of the failure. Even if it does not have another potential use, at the very least, it will be a step on the road to future success. Learning that something doesn't work out will help narrow down the potential ways to go in the future. You may also find one simple flaw that could change the results.

Take everything you have learned from analyzing the failure and try again. As stated above, more than once, the only actual failure is when you stop trying. But the best part about trying again is that your past failure will help show a better way to go or at least a way to avoid it. So, build on your failure, dust yourself off, and get back on the horse.

Leadership

How you define and therefore handle failure depends on your ability to be flexible in your thinking. In addition, it can play a significant role in how you interact with other people and inspire them to perform their tasks more willingly and efficiently. Whether other people see it or not, this is how we define the pecking order in our lives.

Lateral thinking can save time and energy. When the people you work with and those you work with see you using lateral thinking to their benefit, you will go from being just another leader to being a good leader who does their best to work for them. You can even become a great leader because they know you will only demand hard work when it is necessary. They trust you to filter out the BS before it is given to them. In my experience, people like to work hard if there is a good reason with significant results for their efforts.

Efficiency

Creative thinking empowers people by adding strength to their natural abilities, which improves creativity and innovation, which leads to increased productivity and profit. -Edward de Bono

Creativity is about seeing patterns and relationships between elements that may seem obvious in hindsight, but nobody had considered combining existing ideas in such a way before.

One of the most significant developments in the evolution of human communication was the invention of the printing press. Few people know that Johannes Gutenberg didn't just wake up one morning and build a machine that challenged the Roman Catholic Church's monopoly over the production of books.

He combined the essential elements of a wine press, the typesetting process for minting coins, and the wooden blocks used to make playing cards. Adding his own experience as a metalworker brought it all together in a way that changed history. He cast the characters he needed out of metal instead of wood and used a rolling device to ink them. The rest, as they say, is history.

Of course, the concept of lateral thinking was only coined centuries later. However, this doesn't change that the basic principles were responsible for the Renaissance and the Industrial Revolution. People with the ability to step outside the restrictions of conventional thinking have always been the ones to take us off the beaten track and change the world as we knew it.

Communication

In a 2018 study, The Regional Institute of English, South India Ramakrishnan, and Dhanavel used lateral thinking to improve students' ability to communicate concepts in English.

The researchers concluded that lateral thinking plays "a dominant role in helping learners to develop oral communication skills. It enhances fluency and enables effective delivery of language concepts for a better oral presentation."

They also found that it helped students to broaden and change their perceptions.

One of the reasons for this is that exploring alternative ideas requires a more extensive vocabulary than pursuing similar thought patterns. There was also more discussion between team members, which increased the students' confidence in speaking English, their second language.

As you can see, lateral thinking is about a lot more than just an efficient system for problem-solving. It is about changing how we perceive the world and our place in it. As we develop these skills ourselves, we can teach them to our children more quickly. This means that we can shift the basic mentality of humanity in just one generation.

Everyone can be a genius. All it takes is a bit of innovative work instead of hard work.

Enjoy the process.

LATERAL THINKING TECHNIQUES

I do a great deal of work with young children, and if you give a child a problem, he may come up with a highly original solution, because he doesn't have the established route to it. - Edward de Bono

The first step towards changing how we think is to forget what we were taught about how to think.

A systematic process that provides the basic structure of lateral thinking consists of seven fundamental techniques. When these techniques are applied to a problem, situation, or challenge, they will help you find an innovative solution.

I can usually spot the talent in the training group by the first person to make a snide remark about how we're going to follow a formula to learn to avoid formulaic thinking. Whether or not that talent is harnessed successfully depends on their ability to understand the need for boundaries.

Attitude is as important as creativity. It is easy to spot loopholes and argue for the sake of being argumentative. The real challenge lies in using lateral thinking to draw conclusions and solve problems even with limited information. The key to changing how you think lies in connecting new information to the knowledge you have already learned. Being flexible in your thinking is also a valuable leadership skill that allows you to communicate more effectively with people who have different communication styles and perspectives.

The following techniques developed by Edward de Bono in 1971 have proved helpful in approaching problems, focusing on finding solutions and alternatives that may not be discovered through more conventional means.

1. Alternatives

Think of this as the brainstorming stage.

Your goal is to come up with ideas.

Make notes of every option that could solve the problem, even if they don't seem to be practical right now. Don't judge them as negative or positive.

Create a bullet-point list.

Only stop when you can't think of any more ideas.

2. Focus

This is where you start narrowing down your long list of possibilities.

Evaluate each of the ideas on the list:
- What are the pros and cons?
- Is it relevant to the situation at hand?
- How easy is it to implement?
- Use a concrete example to test feasibility.

This process should eliminate some ideas while making others more suitable.

3. Challenge

Find ways to test the remaining ideas. This may inspire new possibilities to test. Try to remember that you are still aiming for creativity. The obvious solution may be the easiest but don't lose sight of the main objective of the exercise - to practice looking beyond the obvious.

Sometimes the ideas that we reject for being too crazy can be the most efficient solutions when we look at them more closely. So, step out of your comfort zone a bit to challenge why some ideas don't appeal to you. You may find that opening your mind to different ways of thinking can lead you to unexpected levels of brilliance.

4. Random Entry

Change your thinking pattern and stimulate new ideas by asking random questions or introducing an unexpected perspective. The aim here is to prevent yourself from getting stuck in a rut. Feel free to go way off on a tangent. You never know where it could lead.

"Sell the sizzle" is now a commonly used marketing term. Even though Elmer Wheeler first used it long before Edward de Bono defined the term lateral thinking, it is an excellent example of this process stage.

While everyone was stuck in the rut of selling products based on logic and function, Wheeler stepped out of the box and introduced the idea of appealing to the emotions of the potential customer.

5. Provocation and Movement

We think the way we have been taught to think. Our parents, friends, neighbors, and classmates were all taught to think the same way. This means that everyone applies the same thought process to the same information to reach the same conclusions. There is very little room for creativity or innovation in this formula. One of the ways to break out of these patterns is to make a statement that assumes that something we take for granted is not true. This provocative statement can seem ridiculous at first. The point is to use a different starting point to generate unexpected results.

The first person who suggested that you could cycle 100 miles without leaving the building would have been considered insane. Now stationary bikes are standard gym equipment.

6. Harvesting

This is the point at which we decide what to use going forward. While it is always valuable to challenge our habitual thinking, every idea can't be a winner. Instead, we must choose the most efficient solution for the problem at hand.

Examine each option to assess how relevant it is to the specific situation in front of you.

- What are the benefits?
- Are there circumstances or factors that could make a provocative suggestion a viable option?
- Are there circumstances or factors that would make the idea irrelevant to the current problem?
- How easy would it be to implement?

You can strike off the ideas that don't meet the criteria based on individual situations rather than preconceived bias.

7. Treatment of Ideas

By now, you should have a reasonable shortlist of solutions to your puzzle. Next, reevaluate the problem from the perspective of each possible solution. This will show you where you have had breakthroughs and which aspects need further thought. You may also see new connections that generate even more possibilities.

You may need to go through the process more than once to find the best solution. Lateral thinking can often yield unexpected results that require testing or verification. These may turn out to be wrong solutions. Sometimes they need to be eliminated. Other times they can inspire a train of thought that leads to the perfect solution.

2

VISUALIZATION AS A PROBLEM-SOLVING TOOL

Creating a picture of the information can often inspire new perspectives on old data. We talk about looking at the bigger picture and seeing things from different points of view. Even the language we use suggests that we are all visual learners or thinkers to some extent. There are many different methods to think of or display ideas, concepts, and problems to make it easier to process information through visualization rather than verbal communication.

In this chapter, we will look at mental visualization, representative visualization, and mind maps as tools in themselves and evaluate their usefulness in lateral thinking.

Mental Visualization

As the name suggests, this process involves creating images in your mind. Close your eyes. What do you see? Most people don't see anything. It's usually just darkness or sometimes a plain color. If you are facing the sun when you close your eyes, maybe you will see a bit of red or yellow. Practice and focus can result in an ability to create detailed, vivid mental images. However, mental images tend to be more abstract, but nevertheless they can be used as a very powerful problem-solving tool.

Even if the mental images are not as clear or as detailed as physically seeing them through our eyes, we still use the same parts of our brain to process the information. This means that we can use mental images to prepare a plan of action for future events.

Mental imagery can also be used as an abstract tool for processing mathematical word problems. For example, if you have three sweets and your friend has five, how many sweets do you have altogether? Most adults would say eight without even thinking about it. When children are learning math, they need to visualize the sweets and count them in their mind's eye. Similarly, we can practice using mental imagery to develop abstract thinking skills until they become second nature.

This is one of the main reasons visualization is so useful in lateral thinking. Practise the exercises below to learn to create pictures in your mind to represent the problems you are trying to solve. Playing with abstract mental images makes it easier to manipulate and combine concepts in creative new ways that would not be possible with linear thought, which follows a step-by-step formula or logical approach. Your mind is a space where you can practice lateral thinking strategies without physical trial and error or practical limitations. You can break the rules of logic, question assumptions, and make connections that can inspire unexpected trains of thought that you would have missed without a mental image. Allowing your mind to wander while visualizing a situation can spark innovative solutions. You will be surprised how easy it is to change the way you think and apply new strategies to every aspect of your life.

Being able to troubleshoot equipment issues from prior experience may not seem like lateral thinking or mental visualization until we look at examples of our work. This is a typical call that I would get on duty as Combat Systems Officer of the Watch (CSOOW)

Lieutenant on watch: System XXX monitor doesn't work; your techs have to fix it.

Me: System XXX monitor doesn't work Aye (Aye is used to confirm that I correctly understand what they are saying). What is the specific symptom you're seeing?

Lieutenant on watch: The screen is black. I checked that it is on. All of your guys have to wake up and work together to fix this because we have something major going on.

Me: Have you tried to turn the screen brightness up? Since it is 0600 (6 am), the night watch probably turned the screen brightness down for navigation reasons.

Lieutenant on watch: Issue resolved

Me: Issue resolved with System XXX monitor Aye.

This sounds like a simple solution, but it takes training in lateral thinking to break out of the habit of blind obedience so that we can:
- ask relevant questions to obtain useful additional information
- evaluate those solutions and link the new information to existing knowledge
- create a clear mental image of the situation at hand

- offer quick, easy solutions to try instead of resorting to conventional solutions that are usually more time or labor-intensive

An inexperienced CSOOW may have accepted the Lieutenant's assumption that the monitor wasn't working and followed instructions to wake up the entire tech team or interrupt their meal before they were about to start a ten (or more) hour shift on duty. But again, lateral thinking can save time and energy.

Mental visualization has even been used to overcome phobias. Mental visualization of the object of fear stimulates the same areas of the brain without the physical threat. This makes it easier to practice different ways of reacting to the fear. In addition, dealing with the abstract representation allows the person to try out other coping mechanisms in a safe space until they are ready to confront their fears physically.

Using Mental Visualization to Solve a Lateral Thinking Puzzle

Puzzle

There is a room with a basket holding six oranges in the center. Six people enter the room, and each takes an orange, but in the end, the basket still contains an orange. How?

Clues

Picture the room in your mind's eye. See the basket in the center and the six oranges inside the basket. Now visualize the six people coming into the room and taking an orange, one at a time. Can you see how the basket can still contain an orange?

If not, reimagine the scenario, but stop after five people have taken an orange each. That leaves one orange in the basket and one person without an orange. How is it possible for them to take the orange, and leave it in the basket simultaneously?

Solution

The last person picked up the basket with the last orange in it, after the other five had taken their oranges.

Mental Visualization Exercises

The best way to master any skill is through practice. Mental visualization is no different. Start by preparing a space where you can minimize distractions. Next, you need to focus entirely on the mental images you create and the thoughts that make them clearer. We will start with simple exercises and move on to more complex visualizations.

Exercise one

Let's start with a highly familiar object to you, like a piece of fruit. I'm going to stick with oranges since we've already talked about them. Feel free to choose something more personal for you. Just remember to keep it simple. The point of this exercise is to practice your focus. Read through my instructions for visualizing an orange and apply the principles to whatever object you choose.

Think of the color and shape of an orange.

Create a basic image in your mind.

See the small, green piece at the top where it used to connect to the tree, picture the vibrant orange skin all the way down to the bump that marks the bottom of the sphere.

Once you can see the basic shape, zoom in. Look closely at the peel of the orange. See each little dimple on the surface. Can you find any creases or blemishes?

Now imagine that you are holding the orange. Run your fingers over the surface. What do those dimples feel like on your skin?

When that information feels real in your mind, take the next step. Imagine what it feels like to peel an orange - the sensation of the peel tearing and the fine spray of juice on your skin. Breathe in the smell of citrus. Keep going until you have removed every piece of the peel. When you look at the orange in your hand, you can see every segment. There are random bits of the pithy white covering left behind.

Stick your thumb into the middle of the orange and break it in half. Feel the juice on your fingers. Pull off a segment. Imagine the moment your teeth break through the surface. Feel the soft insides of the fruit on your tongue as the gush of tangy juice hits your taste buds. Keep chewing. Feel the softened pulp slide down your throat as you swallow. Take another bite.

Keep going until you feel an increase in saliva in your mouth. When this happens, you will know that your mental visualization was strong enough to trick your body into reacting as if you were eating an orange.

Repeat the exercise with different foods. Experiment with things you like and things you find unpleasant. Notice how your body reacts to your visualizations.

Exercise two

Let's move on to something more complex, like visualizing another person. We'll start similarly to the first exercise, but I promise we'll change tactics so you don't have to picture eating them!

The first step is to choose the person you want to visualize. It should be somebody whose appearance is very familiar to you. The easiest would probably be a friend or family member, but you could also choose a favorite character from a movie or any celebrity that you have looked at often.

Start with their face. What color are their eyes? Move out a bit to see the shape of their eye sockets, the texture of their eyelids, and the definition of their eyebrows. Zoom out a bit more to include the nose, mouth, and cheeks. When you can see their entire face clearly, broaden your focus to look at the whole head. Imagine the texture, color, and length of their hair. Keep zooming out gradually until you can see the entire person from head to foot. Do you see them from the front view or in profile? Rotate them around so you can see them from every angle.

Here's where it gets challenging. Once the overall image is stable in your mind, try to change the appearance and their clothes. There is a strong chance that your mind will not cooperate at this stage. It may refuse to make the change or make a different change. You may even lose the original image and have to start from scratch again. This is natural. The aim is to maintain control of the process. If the change you are attempting is too jarring and you lose the picture, don't give up. Just start over again and keep trying for smaller changes. For example, if changing the hair color does not work, try a minor change like making straight hair slightly wavy. If that's still too much, take an inch off the length of the hair.

While similar thought processes can be taught, each person's mind is unique. As you practice, you will find the gradient of change that your mind is willing to accept. Play with that. Explore your potential and take control of your thought processes.

Exercise three

The most advanced stage is to hold and change an environment in your mind, including as many senses as possible. What can you see, hear, smell, taste, and touch in the environment? How much of the sensory input can you change? Let's practice.

Start with an environment that is most familiar to you. For me, that would be the seaside. My instructions will describe the principles of how I experience the visualization of my everyday environment. Then, you can personalize it to any setting that feels natural to you.

Sit comfortably in a quiet space. Focus is essential here, so make sure there are no distractions. Close your eyes. Imagine you are sitting on a rock on the beach. Keeping your eyes closed, see the point where the ocean meets the clear blue sky on the horizon. Feel the hard surface under you and the soft sand between your toes. Maybe tiny wavelets lapping at your toes. Breathe in deeply. Smell the salt in the air. Listen to the sound of the waves and the seagulls. Take a few more deep breaths as you become immersed in those sights, sounds, and smells. Now feel the gentle breeze on your skin. What season is it? Is that breeze warm or cold? Do you need to imagine putting on or taking off a layer of clothing? As you sit there breathing deeply, focus on the more subtle details. Feel the texture of the rock through your clothes. Every bump makes an impression on your skin. There is a vague trace of the smell of the fish that the boats brought in yesterday. The sounds of a family playing in the distance carry over the sounds of the waves and the birds. Sit there for a few more breaths while you soak the information to thoroughly process the scene.

Now imagine getting up to go for a walk around your imaginary environment. Feel the sand shift under your feet. Take a step onto the wet rocks, and their slickness almost makes you stumble. The wind feels stronger now that you are standing up. From this spot, you can now see the family in the distance. As you walk along the rocks, you feel the sea spray splash your legs. You step into a rock pool, and the water is now up to your knees.

Practice visualizing familiar environments in as much detail as possible. Your mental images will become stronger as you gain experience with this type of mental imagery. This will make it easier to explore unfamiliar and even fantastical places in your mind's eye.

Fiction writers have to be exceptionally skilled in this area to take their readers on believable journeys into worlds they have created.

Representative Visualization

Representative visualization is a more concrete way of looking at the information you are given to solve a problem. Instead of visualizing abstract images in your mind, you create a physical object to represent that raw data. For example, the word problem that we looked at earlier with the sweets could be solved by drawing three dots and then another five dots to count how many there are altogether. When we study algebra later, we represent the same problem as:

$$3x + 5x = ?$$

You can use just about anything as a physical representation of a problem. The puzzle using the oranges could also be represented with pieces of paper. First, cut a piece of paper in half and then cut one of those halves into six pieces. Next, crumple each piece until you have six little balls and place them on the other half of the original sheet of paper. This represents the basket and the oranges. Remove one ball at a time to show each orange being removed. Seeing the last ball of paper alone on the big sheet makes it easier to find the solution.

Board games are an excellent example of physical representations. Chess started as a way to plan military strategy. Can you see the representative visualization of games like Risk, Monopoly, and Clue?

Mind Maps

The difference between mind maps and lists is probably the clearest example of how linear and lateral thinking work. Lists and verbal outlines work for linear thinking. Mind maps are diagrams rather than just straightforward, plain text.

The main theme or topic is written at the center of the page. Lines radiate out like spokes on a wheel from the main theme to link the subcategories or ideas on the topic. Each of those outer points can then be broken down further. Information can be added as ideas inspire a new train of thought. Using different colors can link themes or related concepts as the mind map expands. This makes it easier to add further information to subcategories in each part of the mind map and show connections between different ideas. Relationships between ideas and themes become more evident when looking at all the information on one page.

PRACTICE LATERAL THINKING SKILLS

This chapter allows you to test the skills you read about in the first two chapters. I have provided numerous clues to guide you along your lateral thinking journey. Lateral thinking puzzles are not like logic puzzles because they do not have clear right or wrong answers. Often, they will have more than one solution because lateral thinking is thinking about problems from a different point of view. These lateral thinking puzzles cannot be solved using the standard linear thinking style. For that reason, it is easy to become discouraged when you initially draw a blank. I will continue to remind you to focus on your thoughts instead of the solutions.

We will start with questions to shift your thinking away from conventional, habitual paths. The clues provided will help to eliminate some choices while inspiring new thoughts. Visualize the information presented in the clues as you determine how the statements can be factual. Read each statement closely to determine what assumptions you bring to the question. What do you assume happened before the events described in the problem? Could there be different explanations than what you assumed? Is every piece of information relevant, or are there "red herrings" - facts intentionally included to draw your attention away from key points that lead to an obvious solution?

As with many lateral thinking exercises, these puzzles can often best be solved in a collaborative environment. A group of people brainstorming over the solution will bring forth more critical questions needed to solve them. Some of these problems will likely seem deliberately obtuse. The goal is not to get your solutions to match the solutions provided here. It is to change your initial reaction to the problem. Even if your natural response is to look for a logical solution to an illogical question, you can learn a lot when you read the solution and the explanation of why it works.

Each of the puzzles presented below will be followed by questions to ask, clues to help if you are stumped, and then the solution. The questions that you should be asking will bring your attention to specific parts of the problem that can be used to determine the solution. The clues generally add information that could answer questions you might have after considering the puzzle for a while. They also help to eliminate some options while steering you in different directions. These clues may not address all your potential problems but should answer some of the most common ones. If something is ambiguous, use it to your advantage.

Since this is a practice chapter, the format will be slightly different. Let's start with an example that we have already used to give you an idea of how this puzzle process works.

Puzzle

At the center of a room there is a basket that contains six oranges. Six people enter the room, and each one takes an orange, but in the end, the basket still contains an orange. How is that possible?

Questions

Does each person only take one orange?

What do they do with their oranges?

What do they do with the basket?

Clues

Every person had an orange.

There was still one orange in the basket.

You are making one very incorrect assumption.

Not every person had to remove an orange from the basket for each person to have an orange.

Solution

There are two possible solutions here.

We first discussed that the last person picked up the basket with the orange in it.

29

Can you think of another possibility?

Maybe one of the other people saw the empty basket and decided to put their orange back into it.

Now try the rest of the puzzles on your own. Good luck!

Puzzle 1 - Trolley

A woman in a department store fills her shopping cart to the top. Then, she pushes the full trolley out of the store without paying. Customers, staff, and security personnel see her, but nobody tries to stop her or call the police.

Questions

Who is the woman?

What is in the shopping cart?

Why doesn't she pay?

How is this not a crime?

Where does she take the trolley?

Clues

The woman is not a customer.

Her shopping cart was full of items that didn't require payment.

After a few minutes, she returns to the store with an empty shopping cart.

Solution

The woman is an employee of the department store. She is filling the shopping cart with trash and taking it out to the dumpster.

Puzzle 2 - Country Road

A man is walking down a country road, wearing all black clothing. There are no lights on this stretch of road. As he starts to cross the street, a large black car with no lights on comes around the corner and screeches to a stop. How did the car's driver know he was there?

Questions

Does the color of his clothes matter?

Is the color of the car relevant?

Why would the drivers not have the headlights on?

Clues

The driver chose not to turn on their headlights.

The pedestrian saw the car.

Solution

It was daytime.

Puzzle 3 - Tube

A frightened man prepares to enter a giant metal tube, but his fear is on the verge of overcoming him. His wife is there for him, comforting him but not sharing his fear. He enters the tube, and his wife continues to comfort him the entire time. Hours pass until finally; the wife tells her husband that it is time to leave, and his fear finally ebbs. Explain what happened to the man.

Questions

What is the large tube?

How large is the tube?

Was the wife in the tube as well?

Did something happen to the tube when the man was inside it?

Clues

The woman was in the tube with her husband.

The tube was large enough to hold many other people.

Solution

The large tube was an airplane, and the man had a crippling fear of flying. His wife did not share the same fear but comforted her husband during the journey. The problem ends when the plane lands and they disembark.

Without the clue that the wife was in the tube with her husband, another solution to this problem could be an MRI machine. They are large metal tubes but not as large as airplanes, and many people have claustrophobia, the fear of confined spaces.

Puzzle 4 - Toothache

A man went into a party and drank some of the punch. He left early because he had been suffering from a toothache all day. Everyone at the party who drank the punch later died of poisoning. Why did the man not die?

Questions

What was different about him compared to the other guests?

How is his toothache relevant?

What did the other people have in their drinks that he didn't?

Clues

He removed something that would have caused him more pain.

The others consumed more of this as time went by.

Solution

The poison from the punch came from the ice cubes. When the man drank the punch, the ice was fully frozen. He didn't take any ice because it would have worsened his toothache. Gradually, as the ice cubes melted, and the poison was released into the punch.

Puzzle 5 - Presidents

Most people know that the 2nd and 6th presidents were father and son, John Adams and John Quincy Adams, as were the 41st and 43rd presidents, George H. W. Bush and George W. Bush. However, fewer people know that the 22nd and 24th presidents had the same mother and father but were not brothers. Explain how this could be.

Questions

How can they have the same parents without being brothers?

Clues

There has never been a female president of the United States.

Solution

They were the same person: Grover Cleveland. Cleveland was elected in 1884, but he was defeated in his 1888 bid for reelection by Benjamin Harrison, the grandson of former president William Henry Harrison. In 1892, Cleveland was the nominee again and defeated Harrison, becoming the only president to have served non-consecutive presidential terms.

Puzzle 6 - Boxers

Two boxers are in a match scheduled for 12 rounds. (Pure boxing only. There are no kicking or takedowns). One of the boxers gets knocked out after only six rounds, yet neither man throws a punch. How is this possible?

Questions

Is it possible to win a boxing match without throwing a punch?

How else is it possible that no man threw a punch in six rounds?

Clues

If you haven't guessed it already, you are making one huge false assumption.

Solution

Both the boxers were female.

Puzzle 7 - Hotel Room

A man is unpacking his bag in his hotel room when there is a knock on the door. He opens the door to find a woman he has never seen before. She looks surprised and apologizes, saying, "I'm sorry, I thought this was my room."

He becomes suspicious when she goes straight to the elevator and pushes the down button. He calls security immediately to report an intruder in the hotel. How did he know that she was lying and wasn't a guest at the hotel?

Questions

What do you do when you get to the door of your hotel room?

Why would you knock on a door?

Clues

The woman didn't have a key.

The woman didn't hesitate to go to the elevator and push the button.

Solution

The man was immediately suspicious because people don't knock at their hotel room doors. After all, everyone has their own keys. If the woman had lost her key, she would have phoned reception or gone to look for them instead of knocking at the door.

This was confirmed when the woman went straight to the elevator. If she was sharing a hotel room, she would have stopped to check the room number, or tried to call the person she was sharing the with to check that she was in the right place. She would have at least paused to think about her room number or check the rooms on either side. The fact that she went straight to the elevator meant that she knew she wasn't supposed to be on that floor.

Puzzle 8 - Sons

A woman had two sons born on the same hour of the same day of the same year. But they were not twins. How is this possible?

Questions

Do they have other siblings?

How would that affect whether or not they are twins?

Clues

They have at least one other sibling.

They were more than twins.

Solution

Another child was born from the same pregnancy. They are triplets.

Puzzle 9 - Romeo and Juliet

A woman walks into a room and finds Romeo and Juliet lying dead on the floor. Otherwise, the room is empty, except for a table, a puddle, and broken glass on the floor. Windows have blown open in the storm, and the curtains are flapping around in a strong wind.

Questions

How does the woman know Romeo and Juliet?

Where did the broken glass come from?

Clues

The broken glass is in the puddle.

The table is close to the window.

Solution

Romeo and Juliet are the woman's pet goldfish. Their bowl broke when the curtains knocked it off the table, resulting in the puddle and the broken glass. Romeo and Juliet were fish out of the water and died because they couldn't breathe.

Puzzle 10 - Car

A man and a woman race down the street in their cars at breakneck speeds. The car comes to a stop, and the man bolts out of the car and returns in a hurry. By the time he gets back to the car, the woman is dead, and a person the man had never met was in the car with her body. How is this possible?

Questions

Did you initially assume they were racing against each other?

Where are they going?

Why did the man leave and then quickly return?

What could cause a woman to die so quickly?

Who is the stranger?

Where did they come from?

Clues

The man and woman were husband and wife.

They were in the same car.

The stranger was with them throughout the journey

The stranger did not intend to kill the woman.

Solution

The woman was pregnant and going into labor, so the man was driving her to the hospital as quickly as possible. Once they reached the hospital, he jumped out of the car to get a wheelchair for his wife. By the time he returned, the baby was born, the baby is the stranger, and his wife had died in labor.

CHAPTER 4

WARM-UP PUZZLES

This chapter focuses on simple logic puzzles. Here, the aim is to question your basic assumptions, look for alternatives, and trace a new train of thought to its logical conclusion. The first section lists the puzzles. The clues in the second section are given in the form of questions to stimulate a broader range of thoughts rather than to narrow them down to a specific thought. The final section allows you to compare your solutions with our solutions. It does not matter to us if you come up with different solutions. For now, do not worry about what's right or wrong. The aim is to move out of your habitual patterns of thought. Give yourself a fair chance to think about each puzzle before looking at the solutions. Challenge yourself to find more than one solution, as in the example. You will find yourself laughing out loud at some of the unexpected solutions. Have fun.

Get comfortable with this format. Your clues are now the questions to guide your thinking. It will stay the same for the rest of the puzzle chapters.

Puzzles

1. Ernie walked in the door and said to his wife, "I shot two eagles today." She was disappointed and told him that he could have shot more. How could a wife want her husband to shoot more eagles?

2. A teenager told his mom he was joining a band. She happily asked for more information. When she heard his reply, she was upset and said he was looking for trouble. What could the boy have said to change his mom's attitude?

3. Two amateur golfers shot a hole-in-one four times on the same eighteen-hole course. How?

4. She lived on Campus but had never attended college. Why?

5. Christine sat in her car watching the rain, but her windshield was completely dry. How is this possible?

6. Steve dropped a full cup on the floor in a crowded room. Why did nobody react?

7. Paul saw the stop sign but didn't slow down even though other cars had stopped at the sign. How did he not hit anybody?

8. How is it possible for Kelly to celebrate her fifth birthday in her sophomore year of college?

9. A man and his dog are on opposite sides of a river. There is no boat or bridge. How does the dog cross the river without swimming when the man calls him?

10. How can a man marry three women in one day and still be single?

Clues

1. a. How can you shoot without a gun?
   b. When is an eagle not a bird?

2. a. Think about different contexts for the word band.
   b. What kind of group could the son join that would get him into trouble?

3. a. Where do amateur golfers play more often than professionals?
   b. What would make it easier to shoot a hole in one?

4. a. Does *Campus* have to refer to a college?
   b. What else can you live on?

5. a. How can you watch the rain without getting wet?
   b. What protects a car from the weather?

6. a. What kind of cup is likely to be dropped without attracting attention?
   b. Who uses this kind of cup?

7. a. Where did the other cars stop?
   b. Why would Paul keep going?

8. a. How old is an average sophomore?
   b. Can somebody be 20 but only have had five birthdays?

9. a. How do you cross a river without swimming?

   b. When can you walk on water?

10. a. How do you marry a woman but not make her your wife?

b. Who can marry other people without getting married?

Solutions

1. Ernie is a golfer. An *eagle* in golf means being two under par for each hole. As a professional, Ernie should have been able to shoot more than two eagles on an 18-hole course.

2. The son was joining a band of criminals.

3. They were playing on a miniature golf course.

4. The street she lived on was called Campus.

5. The car was parked in a garage.

6. Steve was a toddler who dropped his sippy cup.

7. The stop sign was at a T-Junction, facing away from the street Paul was on. The other cars had to stop and wait for Paul to pass before they could turn onto that street.

8. Kelly was born on the 29th of February, so she is 20 but has only had five birthdays.

9. The dog could walk across the river because the water was frozen solid.

10. He is a priest.

CHAPTER 5

LEVEL UP

Now that you have practiced questioning your basic assumptions, let's move further out of the box. Some of the puzzles in this chapter refer to situations that may not be familiar to you. The aim is to draw you out of your mechanical

43

responses. Don't be disappointed if they feel too difficult. Practice using the techniques you learned in the first two chapters to try to understand these situations. These puzzles were vague and open to multiple possible solutions. It is quite likely that you would have come up with different solutions to the ones I provided. Try to be objective in assessing the quality of your thought process by looking for flaws in your logic. This approach can be more beneficial to learning lateral thinking than simply getting all the solutions right.

Again, it doesn't matter if your solutions are the same as mine. The aim is to become more aware of how you approach the questions. Don't think about it as being right or wrong. Instead, try to follow the train of thought that leads to different solutions.

Puzzles

1. A guy walks into a dark room and turns a handle. About an hour later, he is surprised by a knock at the door. A woman walks in and talks to him. He thanks her for disturbing him. As soon as he starts turning the handle again, she thanks him and leaves.

2. A man is late for work. He rushes into a train car without thinking, apologizes to the other passengers for his mistake, and leaves in a hurry. Then he gets into another car on the same train to arrive at the correct destination.

3. A woman is sitting down. A man opens the door and turns on a light. She looks out the window and shouts at him to turn it off again.

4. A man jumps off a balcony aiming to land on a horse but ends up in a car instead. How could this happen?

5. The doorbell rings. A woman opens the door and answers a question. The next day her bicycle is covered in shaving cream.

6. A man plays a tune. Somebody screams. People run away. A man has to kill his friend.

7. A man wearing a bird mask declares the cause of the death of a family.

8. A man walks into a cave, points at a wall, and taps his chest. When he walks out of the cave again, a group of strangers follows him, with whoops of joy.

9. A child discovers something in the garden. She checks up on it excitedly every day for weeks. One day she arrives to find it broken, but she is happy instead of getting upset.

10. A man sits quietly on a bench with his daughter. He suddenly sits up and asks her if she heard a tapping noise. She says that she didn't. He listens carefully again, then tells her to call the police.

11. You are driving a bus. When you leave the station, there are four men and five women on board. At the first stop, three teenagers get on. At the second stop, two women get on, and three men get off. At the third stop, three kids and their mom get on, and nobody gets off. The bus is yellow, and it is warm outside. What color is the bus driver's hair?

Clues

1. a. What requires turning a handle in a dark room?
   b. Why would he be grateful to be disturbed?

2. a. When was it a mistake to get into a different car on the same train?
   b. Why would he apologize to the other passengers?

3. a. What changes when you turn on an inside light?
   b. Why is it significant that she could see out of the window?

4. a. Why would a man want to jump off a balcony and land on a horse?

b. What is the relationship between the horse and the car?

5. a. When do you answer a question on your doorstep?

   b. How does a wrong answer result in something unexpected happening the next day?

6. a. Is the scream related to the tune?

   b. Who is the friend?

7. a. Who used to wear a bird mask?

   b. What could be the same cause of death for a whole family?

8. a. What was on the wall?

   b. Why would strangers be happy to follow him?

9. a. What transforms in a garden that would be exciting enough for a child to check it every day?

   b. What does the breakage indicate?

10. a. Why would he hear something that she couldn't hear?

    b. What could tapping communicate?

11. a. What is the key question?

    b. Which facts are irrelevant to your answer?

Solutions

1. The guy is a projectionist at an old-fashioned movie theater. He falls asleep, and the film soon stops. A woman in the audience goes up to the projection room to find out what happened. Her knock wakes him up, and he can continue screening the movie. They are both happy with the outcome.

2. This puzzle is set in segregated America in the 1960s, when Jim Crow laws were still enforced. At the time, there were separate train cars for white people and black people. A black man wasn't paying attention because he was in a hurry, and he stepped into a whites-only car by mistake. As soon as he saw the other passengers, he realized his

mistake. He had to apologize because he might have been arrested if they thought he had got into their carriage on purpose. He then got into the blacks-only train car and got to the right destination at the right time because he was still on the same train.

3. They were detectives on a stakeout. When her partner turned the light on, the suspects outside would have been able to see them. It was important that the light stayed off, so that they would not attract unwanted attention.

4. The man was a stunt double on a movie set. They were filming the getaway scene in a Wild West bank heist. He was supposed to jump off the balcony, land on the horse, and ride off. There was a convertible driving behind the horse with camera equipment to capture the scene. A loud noise spooks the horse as the man jumps. The film car speeds up, and the man lands in it instead of landing on the horse.

5. It's Halloween. The question she answered was, "Trick or Treat?" She refused to hand over the candy. The children at the door responded by playing a trick on her the next day. They covered her bicycle in shaving cream.

6. The man was a snake charmer. He played a tune on his flute. As the cobra came out of his basket, it attacked somebody in the audience. The woman screamed, and the rest of the audience ran away terrified. The man had to kill the snake that he had considered a friend.

7. In 17th century England, plague doctors wore masks with a beak-like pocket to hold herbs to purify the air entering their noses. They would have recognized when an entire family had been killed by the Bubonic plague and had the authority to proclaim the cause of death.

8. The man is a Neanderthal. He left his clan and wanted to join a new one. He decided that the best way to be accepted into a new tribe would be to offer them food. He killed an

antelope but didn't have the language to communicate this to them. He pointed to a cave drawing of a hunter killing an antelope and then indicated himself to show that he had also killed an antelope. They knew that he wouldn't be telling them about it unless he wanted to share it with them. They were happy to welcome a new hunter to their tribe.

9. The child had found a caterpillar in the garden. She watched it grow and build a cocoon. She checked on it every day until she found the cocoon empty and broken. She knew that this meant that the caterpillar had turned into a butterfly and flown away.

10. The man had an overdeveloped sense of hearing to compensate for his blindness. He asked his daughter if she could hear the tapping so that he understood how loud it was. The fact that she could hear it confirmed that the sound was muffled because it was coming from underground. The tapping pattern was repeated continuously. When he listened again, he knew that it was Morse code for SOS.

11. It's your hair color. The puzzle starts with you being the bus driver.

CRIME SCENE
INVESTIGATIONS

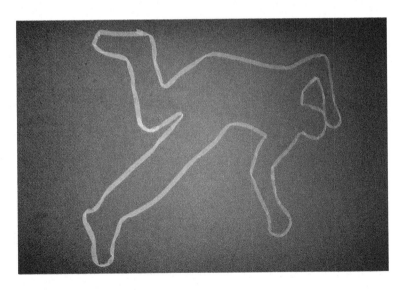

The puzzles in this chapter help you to evaluate information and draw conclusions. Some facts are deliberately misleading, ambiguous, or open to misinterpretation. Finding plausible explanations for these situations will test your willingness to leap to conclusions. Consider the most far-fetched ideas you can imagine.

Puzzles

1. Men were shot because they were wearing blue.

2. Two people buy cigarettes from a little store just as the owner starts the process of closing up. As they leave, they see him setting the alarm very slowly. They've barely walked two blocks when they hear an explosion. They turn around and realize that it is their fault.

3. A woman listens to a clock chime and realizes that something has been stolen from her store.

4. A man puts a coin into an old-fashioned public phone. He gets arrested for vandalism very soon afterward.

5. Many people are killed when a chain is pulled.

6. Somebody falls off a high cliff above the ocean but doesn't drown.

7. Two law enforcement officers chase the thief. After a few hours, they give up and walk home while the thief escapes. What did he steal, and how did he get away?

8. A woman walks past a house and hears a voice screeching, "Stop it! You're killing me!" She calls the cops. When they arrive, all they find is a person who died of a heart attack, birdseed, and the belongings of many missing people.

9. A man reports a missing person at 12:05 pm. He insists that he knows the person is in trouble because of something he didn't hear. He also claims that the disappearance happened between 6 am and 12:00 pm. When the police find the body, they know that the caller was right before the coroner confirms the time of death.

10. A man leaves his door open overnight during a very hot summer. The next day he takes a dog for a morning walk. When he tries to cross the street, he gets hit by a car.

Clues

1. a. Why would groups of people wear the same color?

   b. How would that result in people wanting to kill them?

2. a. Does it matter what the customers bought?

   b. Why was the owner having trouble setting the alarm? He was doing it slowly.

3. a. Where would you hear clocks chime?

   b. What could be significant about her recognizing the sound?

4. a. Is there a reason the question specifies that it was a coin-operated phone?

   b. Why would somebody vandalize a phone box after putting in a coin?

5. a. When was pulling chains the most efficient way to move objects?

   b. Where was this used as a defense?

6. a. What is necessary for drowning?

   b. Where would a person land when jumping off a cliff?

7. a. What did the person steal?

   b. How did this help them escape?

8. a. Whose voice did the woman hear?

   b. There were missing people's belongings in the house?

9. a. What was the man expecting to hear?

   b. How could he be so specific about the times?

10. a. Is it relevant why the door was open?

    b. Where was the dog when the man was trying to cross the street?

Solutions

1. Union soldiers wore blue uniforms in the American Civil War. This is how Confederate soldiers were able to

identify and kill them. This puzzle can refer to any conflict situation, real or role played, like paintball or computer games, where one side is identified by the color blue.

2. The two people were the technicians responsible for installing a new security system at the store. The owner was setting up the alarm slowly because it was the first time he had done it. The technicians were still there at closing time, which meant they had worked late. They rushed through parts of the job and ended up with electrical faults. They realized their mistake when the faulty wiring resulted in an explosion. The fact that they bought cigarettes was a red herring.

3. The woman owns an antique clock store. She figures that the best place to hide a valuable family heirloom is in plain sight. It is simply marked not for sale. She places it pressed up against another clock in such a way that prevents the other clock from chiming. When she hears that special clock chime, she knows that the family heirloom has been removed.

4. The person is a collector of unusual coins. He had just collected a new one and was admiring it while making a phone call on his way home. When his time ran out on the call, he accidentally put the rare coin into the slot instead of the quarter he was also holding. As soon as he realized his mistake, he panicked. He got the tire iron out of his car and tried to break open the coin box to get back his special coin. People saw him damaging the phone box and called the police, who came along and arrested him for vandalism.

5. Medieval English castles had drawbridges that opened and shut by pulling on a chain. When the castle came under attack, its defenders waited until the attacking force was halfway across the drawbridge and then pulled the chain to draw the bridge up to close it. As the drawbridge rose, the men and horses fell off into the moat where they

drowned. Those who didn't fall into the moat ended up inside the castle, where they were quickly overpowered by castle soldiers.

6. It was low tide. They landed on the rocks below and were injured by the fall instead of drowning.

7. The person was a horse thief and stole two horses. The people following him were also on horseback, but after a few hours, their mounts became tired. The thief could swap horses since they had stolen two. The horse that wasn't carrying his weight was still fresh. The pursuers only had one horse each and had to walk back home leading their exhausted horses.

8. The dead man had a parrot. When she saw that the man was dying, she wanted to get attention so that someone would help. She was screeching phrases that she had heard many times before. She knew how to say, "Stop it!" and "You're killing me." because the man was a serial killer who had been bringing his victims to his house. That's why the police also found the belongings of missing people.

9. It is a rural area in England. A man, who was a priest, had become disillusioned with the world and his religion. He rang the church bells as usual at 6 a.m. that morning. After breakfast he went for a walk and threw himself off a cliff, and into the sea below, where he drowned. A farmer living nearby was awake early and heard the 6 a.m. church bells as usual. However, he noticed that the 12-noon bells had not rung. That's how he could be so specific about the time.

10. The man is blind. He takes his guide dog with him for a walk every morning. Last night when he left the door open, a stray dog wandered into his home. The stray dog was of a similar size to his guide dog. The man put the collar and lead on the stray dog instead of his guide dog. The stray dog did not know how to lead the blind man across the road safely, resulting in him being struck by a car.

CHAPTER 7

SECRET, ADVENTURE, AND MISCELLANEOUS

By now, you should be able to start seeing alternative explanations and drawing outlandish conclusions. So, let's test your skills on a few more seemingly inexplicable situations. How far have you stretched your mental comfort zone?

Puzzles

1. A lady presses something. In a few seconds, her life is in danger. She narrowly escapes death but gets what she came for and leaves happy.

2. Two guys get onto a ship and travel to America. They meet the captain while onboard but are arrested as soon as the ship reaches its destination.

3. The cutting down of a tree marks the end of civilization.

4. What seems to be seven but is only one?

5. A man goes into an empty cage. After a few minutes of loud noise, the audience bursts into applause.

6. Three men sit close together at a seaside bar, talking with their heads down, looking at a piece of paper. Another customer hears the words "Dead man" and becomes suspicious. He follows the trio when they leave the pub. They walk slowly along the beach and then start digging. The man calls the police, but they don't find a body.

7. A man escapes death when the sky suddenly goes dark for a short while.

8. A man is being chased through a jungle. With just a knife, he kills a number of his pursuers at once and makes sure that nobody else can follow him.

9. A man is lying in a puddle wearing a scuba suit, but he is a mile away from the ocean.

10. A young doctor has to wear a clean shirt every day. He takes his shirts to the laundromat every Monday morning and picks them up exactly one week later. What is the minimum number of shirts that the doctor needs to own to have a clean shirt to put on every morning?

Clues

1. a. What could she push that would place her in danger?
   b. Where would she risk her life to get something valuable?

2. a. How did they meet the captain?

   b. Why were they arrested?

3. a. What tree is important enough to end something?

   b. What is the effect of not having trees?

4. a. Is the number 7 significant?

   b. What separates appearance from reality?

5. a. How does the man enter the empty cage?

   b. What makes a loud noise that would result in applause from an audience?

6. a. What is on the piece of paper that they are looking at?

   b. When does "dead man" not refer to a corpse?

7. a. When does the sky only go dark for a short time?

   b. Think about the superstitions surrounding these occurrences.

8. a. What can he cut that would kill many people at once?

   b. How would he also stop others from copying his moves?

9. a. Where would a person usually be scuba diving?

   b. How could he be moved so quickly that he doesn't have time to remove his scuba gear?

10. a. Why are eight shirts not enough?

    b. How long are the clothes at the laundromat?

Solutions

1. The woman is an explorer or an archaeologist. She presses part of the wall in an ancient tomb, and the wall slides open to reveal a room. It is booby-trapped, and at that moment, a sharp pendulum swings through the air and narrowly misses the explorer, embedding itself into the opposite wall. She is then free to walk into the room and retrieve the ancient relic she sought.

2. They are stowaways and have not paid for tickets.

3. The last tree is cut down on Easter Island. (Scientific evidence, including pollen analysis, has shown that the Rapa Nui islanders destroyed their society through deforestation due to cutting down vast swathes of trees to construct wooden platforms for transporting and working on the huge Moai heads. The lack of trees led to the disappearance of birds and other animals from the island and, therefore, all their food sources. Civil disorder and starvation ensued, and they eventually all died out.)

4. It is a rainbow. It looks like it's made up of seven different colors, but in reality, it's made from just white light, which is refracted at different angles depending on wavelength.

5. He is a stunt motorcyclist performing the Wall of Death.

6. The trio are pirates and have found a treasure map. They were referring to a "dead man's chest," which is said to be buried somewhere nearby. They follow the map and start digging to find the buried treasure.

7. Sometime in the 19th Century or earlier, an explorer was captured by an undiscovered tribe in South America. They are about to sacrifice the explorer to the Sun God when a solar eclipse occurs. They take this as a sign that their captive should be released.

8. He has walked over a rope suspension bridge across a ravine. He uses the knife to cut the rope securing the bridge. His side of the bridge falls into the ravine, and nobody can use it to follow him across.

9. A tornado picked him up out of the ocean and carried him a few miles before dropping him again.

10. He has to have 15 shirts. There are seven dirty shirts at the laundromat. He needs seven clean shirts to wear until he picks them up, and the shirt he wears on Monday when he goes to the laundromat makes a total of fifteen. You could

argue that he could get by with fourteen if he wears a dirty shirt Monday morning when he goes to the laundromat and changes into one of the clean shirts he picked up.

CHAPTER

8

CAN YOU EXPLAIN IT?

Can you find reasonable explanations for the seemingly inexplicable situations listed below? It should be easier for you to question your assumptions and look for alternatives. You should also be familiar with evaluating information by now. This chapter provides plenty of practice with both. Some of these puzzles require extremely unconventional thought processes.

Puzzles

1. A wealthy mother arrives at her son's hotel with her dog and announces that she is bankrupt.

2. A man rode into town on Friday. He stayed for two nights and then left on Friday. How do you explain this?

3. A man goes into a saloon and asks the bartender for a drink of water. The bartender hears something in the man's question and pulls out a shotgun and points it at the man instead. The man thanks the bartender, sits down at the counter, and orders whiskey instead of water. The bartender puts the gun away and pours him a shot of whiskey. How do you explain this?

4. A set of twins celebrated their birthdays, but on different days. One of the twin's birthdays was on Tuesday. The other twin's birthday was two days later, on Thursday. Their mother's labor only lasted six hours. How is this possible?

5. A man is driving his car and hears something unusual on the radio. He then pulls over to the side of the road and calls the police. Why did he do this?

6. A woman is walking along confidently, listening to music. The woman suddenly drops dead very soon after the music stops. How did she die?

7. A man is lying dead in a snowy field with a pack on his back. There are no footprints to or from his body. How did he die?

8. Sylvester lies dead with a piece of metal flat across his back. His favorite food is just out of reach. How did he die?

9. The phone at the reception desk rings during a bank robbery. The armed robbers are still filling up their bags.

One of them orders the receptionist to answer the phone so as not to raise any suspicions. The caller was the receptionist's mother. Everyone in the bank heard, "Mom is it an emergency? I'll call you later when I can talk for a minute, or I'll help you when I get home." The robbers were satisfied that the call was innocent and went back to what they were doing. The police arrived a few minutes later and arrested the armed men. How did they know there was a robbery?

10. A secretary calls the police when she can't get into her boss's office. The door was locked from the inside, with the key still in the lock. The police break into the room. The man is found hanging from the ceiling in the middle of the room. He is wearing shoes. The most unusual thing in the room is a hammer lying in a puddle of water. Can you explain what happened?

Clues

1. a. How did the mother go from being wealthy to being bankrupt just by arriving at a hotel?
   b. Why is the dog relevant?

2. a. How did the man arrive in town?
   b. Can his mode of transport be relevant?

3. a. What did the bartender hear?
   b. Why did he pull out his shotgun?

4. a. How could their birthdays be so far apart?
   b. Why is the length of labor relevant?

5. a. What did the man hear on the radio?
   b. Why would that make him call the police?

6. a. Where was she walking?
   b. How is the end of the music related to her death?

7. a. What is the pack on his back?

b. Is it possible to end up in a field without leaving footprints?

8. a. Who is Sylvester?

   b. What is the metal bar on his back?

9. a. How could the receptionist get a different message to her mom?

   b. What words would she have used to drop hints without alerting the robbers?

10. a. How could the door be locked from the inside?

    b. Why is the puddle significant?

Solutions

1. The woman was playing Monopoly with her family. The dog was her token. She landed on the street with a hotel belonging to her son. Even though she also had a lot of money, it wasn't enough to pay the rent, and she had to declare bankruptcy.

2. The man rode into town on a horse whose name was Friday.

3. The bartender heard the man hiccup. He realized that the man wanted water to stop the hiccups. Unexpectedly pointing a gun at him would give a fright and stop the hiccups faster. When the hiccups stopped, the man didn't need the water anymore, so he ordered the whiskey that he wanted.

4. The mother went into labor on the 28th of February. One of the twins was born before midnight. The other was born after midnight, so the second twin's birthday was on the 1st of March. Every leap year their birthdays are separated by an extra day - the 29th of February.

5. The man heard a song skip and start from the beginning again. He was a DJ who had set up a playlist that was long enough to give him an alibi for killing his wife. When he

heard the glitch, he knew that he no longer had an alibi because he would have responded if he had been in the studio. He called the police to hand himself in.

6. The woman was a blind tightrope walker. She had a specific piece of music that was perfectly timed for her to step safely off the rope at the end. She had practiced enough to become completely confident. A rival stopped the music early. The blind woman didn't know how far she was from the end of the rope. She panicked and fell to her death.

7. The pack on his back is a parachute that didn't open when he jumped out of a plane. He died as soon as he landed in the middle of the field.

8. Sylvester was a mouse killed when he tried to get the cheese.

9. The receptionist used the mute button to block out some of the words.

   "Mom, is it an emergency? I'll call you later when I can talk for a minute or I'll help you when I get home."

   What her mom heard was, "Mom. Emergency. Call. For. Help."

10. The man stood on a block of ice to attach the rope to the ceiling. The noose tightened as the ice melted, forming the puddle.

INFERENCE PUZZLES

The simplest way of describing inference puzzles is that they test your ability to read between the lines. Inference is a mental procedure where you can reach a conclusion based on more than the evidence. It requires existing knowledge related to the evidence that has been given. Finding the solution depends on your ability to form connections between the question and your understanding of the world.

This chapter will test how far out of the box you can go while ensuring your solution remains relevant to the context of the puzzle. You need to be able to evaluate your solutions critically to assess the accuracy of your solution from multiple perspectives.

This chapter doesn't include clues. The aim is not to find a solution or even multiple solutions. Instead, you are trying to evaluate the solutions that you find on your own.

Example:

A man's idea of heaven was a tropical beach with a nudist area. When he got there, he was able to identify Adam and Eve immediately. How did he do that?

Solution:

He identified them because they were the only people without belly buttons.

Here's the real challenge:

An alternate solution suggested that the man was either Cain or Abel. As Adam and Eve's sons, they would have recognized their parents. Can you evaluate this solution and explain why it is not an option?

The solution is at the end of the chapter.

Puzzles

1. There is a fishing trawler, with a ladder in it, leaning against a wall at the harbor. There are five oars and two fishing nets

in the trawler. The distance between two consecutive steps on the ladder is one meter. If waves lashing against the wall rise half a meter every half hour, how much time will pass before six steps of the ladder are under the waves?

2. George was walking down the street when a stranger shot him in the stomach. Witnesses said that the suspect had dark hair and was wearing a blue jacket. Sarah came forward as a witness and was asked to identify the killer from a line-up. In her statement, she said, "I was enjoying my cappuccino at a sidewalk table, so I had the perfect view. George was walking down the opposite side of the street, with his hands in his pockets. Suspect number three was following him, but he was wearing a jacket. He must have taken it off when it got covered in blood." The police officers arrested her immediately. How did they know she was lying?

3. A Japanese ship was out on the open sea. The captain took off his watch and wedding ring and put them down on a table before going into the shower. When he returned, his valuables were missing. Five people had access to the table. The captain called all the suspected crew members in for questioning. He asked each one where they were and what they were doing for the last fifteen minutes.

The cook, wearing a heavy overcoat, said, "I was in the cold storage room getting meat for cooking."

The engineer arrived with a torch and said, "I was working on the generator engine."

The seaman said, "I was on deck correcting the flag, which was upside down."

The navigation officer arrived late and said, "I am on night watch, so I was sleeping in my cabin."

The lie was so evident that the captain could identify the thief instantly.

4. Your last good ping-pong ball fell into a narrow metal pipe buried a foot into concrete. The tools you have are your tennis paddle, your shoelaces, and your full plastic water bottle, which does not fit into the pipe?

5. A teacher gives three clever students in her class a challenge: she writes down three different numbers on three index cards and has each student hold up one of the cards to their forehead so that they can't see their card, but everyone else can.

   She tells them each card has a different number and that two of the numbers add up to the third number and asks them to figure out their number without sharing the numbers they see.

   Ava sees Sid has 40 on his forehead, and Vlad has 60 on his forehead.

   Ava says, "I don't know my number."

   Vlad says, "I don't know my number."

   Before Sid can say anything, Ava realizes she can now figure out her number! So what is Ava's number?

6. A man shot two arrows at its center and missed both times. He swung a sword once at its center and hit it twice. What is it?

7. Three friends decide to split the cost of hiring a cleaner. The agency charges them $30, so they each hand over a $10 bill.

   Later the agency discovers the rate was $25 instead of $30. So, they send the cleaner with $5 to reimburse the friends.

   It's hard to split $5 three ways, reasons the cleaner, so he gives the friends $1 each and keeps $2 for himself as a tip.

   But wait – each friend paid $9 for a total of $27, and the cleaner pocketed $2. That's 27 + 2 = 29, whereas they initially handed over $30. So, where did the missing dollar go?

8. A grandmother, two mothers, and two daughters went shopping together, and everyone bought one purse each. How many purses did they bring home altogether?

9. A bike rider is traveling north at 25 mph; a car passes the bike rider going north at 40 mph. At the same time, the bike rider passes a jogger running north at 5 mph. Which will move away from the bike rider at a faster pace, the car, or the jogger?

Solutions

1. The trawler rises with the waves, so none of the steps will go underwater.

2. If the suspect were following George, he would have been behind him, making it impossible to shoot him in the stomach.

3. The Japanese flag is a white background with a red circle precisely in the middle. Nobody would notice if it were upside down. The seaman was the thief.

4. Fill the pipe with water so that the ball floats to the top.

5. Ava sees 40 and 60, so she knows her number must be 20 or 100, but she doesn't know which. Vlad sees Ava's number and 40. If Ava's number were 20, Vlad would see 20 and 40, which would mean his number was 20 or 60 – except he knows the numbers are different, so his number must be 60. Since Vlad could not figure out his number, Ava's number couldn't have been 20, so Ava's number must be 100.

6. Any object with a hole in the center, including a doughnut, a bagel, a ring, or a tire.

   Since these have holes in the center, shooting arrows at the center would hit nothing, but swinging a sword would hit it twice.

7. There is no missing dollar.

You cannot add the cleaner's $2 "tip" to the $27 that the three friends paid because how much they paid already includes that tip – this would be double-counting. So, the three friends ended up paying $27, including $25 to the agency and $2 to the cleaner, which adds up.

If you want to figure out where the $30 went, you should instead start with the amount that the agency received ($25), add the amount the cleaner received ($2), and add the amount the friends received back ($3), which indeed gets you to $30.

8. The grandmother is also a mother, and the mother is also a daughter, so there are only three women. They also each had the purse that they carried when they left home. So that means they brought home six purses.

9. The jogger, because the difference in speed is more significant between the jogger and bike rider than the car and the bike rider.

Cain and Abel Solution:

Cain killed Abel, so he went to hell instead of heaven so it couldn't be him. Abel was killed before Adam and Eve died. They wouldn't have been there yet when he got there. In fact, there might not have been a concept of heaven yet.

CHAPTER 10

FUN WITH FRIENDS

It would help you to know that lateral thinking is about more than finding efficient ways to solve problems. Lateral thinking is about changing the way we think, and it challenges our knowledge, attitudes, and the way we see the world. Instead of competing, we learn to find ways to inspire each other. Leadership becomes about the way we communicate with each other rather than blind obedience to a command chain.

One on One

The first set of puzzles in this section takes the form of a twenty questions type of game. Copy one puzzle and its solution on a separate piece of paper. You can make more than one copy of each puzzle or use puzzles from other chapters or other sources for larger groups. Fold the pieces of paper and put them into a box. Students play in pairs. Player One from each team picks a puzzle. They read the question to their partner as many times as necessary. Player Two then starts to ask questions. Player One is only supposed to answer either "Yes" or "No." They may choose to be more helpful with clues like, "You're getting closer." Player Two can request to have the puzzle read to them again.

You can build communication skills by sticking to yes or no answers so that the players can practice being more observant of non-verbal cues such as body language, tone of voice, eye contact, etc.

When Player Two guesses the solution, they draw another puzzle from the box and swap roles to give Player One the chance to guess.

The puzzles here describe a situation with unexpected outcomes, missing relevant information, or containing red herrings (irrelevant information with the specific purpose of distracting you from the solution). The solutions are answers that provide a reasonable explanation of the situation. There may be more than one correct solution. The person answering the question may consult with a trainer if they think that the player who is guessing may have found an equally plausible solution to the one that was given.

Guidelines for using fewer questions.

Break down each part of the puzzle into segments of information. Consider what you've learned about the types of assumptions that you made in previous chapters. You can use the following list of categories to narrow down relevant information.

- Location - Country/environment/setting
- Time period
- Season/weather/climate
- Job descriptions
- Motivation
- Alternatives

Puzzle 1 - Cash

A lady approaches a counter and hands over a lot of cash. She receives absolutely nothing in return and simply turns around and walks away. Why doesn't she complain?

Solution 1

She is at a bank to deposit cash.

Puzzle 2 - Doors

A man performs the same job at the same time every day. He opens a lot of doors, leaves them open for an hour, then locks them all again.

Solution 2

He is a prison guard. He lets prisoners out for their exercise for an hour a day.

Puzzle 3 - Skyscraper

A woman spends all day moving from one floor of a skyscraper to another but never uses the stairs or an elevator.

Solution 3

She is a window cleaner. She moves up and down the outside of the building using abseiling equipment.

Puzzle 4 - Craftsman

A craftsman can make one of these for absolutely anyone. But, if he does make one for himself, he won't be aware of using it.

Solution 4

He is a coffin maker.

Puzzle 5 - King

A missing king prevents people from enjoying their evening's entertainment.

Solution 5

A king is missing from either a deck of playing cards or a chess set.

Puzzle 6 - Child

A child throws something away. This benefits people a century later.

Solution 6

The child throws an apple core into an empty field while she is walking by. A tree grows. Over the years, more trees have grown from the original tree to create an orchard where many people can pick apples.

Puzzle 7 - Lights Dim

The lights dim while a couple is eating. They show no surprise. Their only response is to stop talking. They still don't react when the lights go out.

Solution 7

They arrived early at a movie theater. The lights dimmed when the trailers started and went out when the movie started.

Puzzle 8 - New Planet

A woman disappears soon after observing a new planet.

Solution 8

She is an astronaut in a spaceship on a mission to find a habitable planet. When she discovers a possible option, she steps into a transportation device and is beamed onto its surface.

Puzzle 9 - Two Friends

Two friends are playing together at a park. They get sopping wet. While they are drying off, without towels, two people approach them at the same time. As they get close, they raise their voices before leading the friends away in opposite directions.

Solution 9

The two friends are dogs. They go for a swim in a pond at the park just before it's time to go home. They shake off the water while their humans try to attach their leashes. The humans squeal when they get splashed. Then they lead their own dog home.

Puzzle 10 - Picnic Basket

A man puts his picnic basket down on the ground. He goes for a walk, meaning to come back later to eat his lunch. When he returns to the same spot, he sees the basket out of reach in the distance, and he knows that nobody has touched it, but his meal is ruined. How was the basket moved?

Solution 10

The man had placed the basket on the sand at the beach during low tide. By the time he returned from his walk, it was high tide. The waves have washed his picnic basket out to sea. He could still see it bobbing on the waves in the distance. Even if he could swim out to get it, the saltwater would have ruined the food.

The puzzles below are perfect for larger groups. They demonstrate how the lateral thinking process can inspire group members and highlight leadership skills. Each puzzle has more than one plausible solution. The goal is to find as many solutions as possible. This requires applying all seven of Edward de Bono's techniques.

1) Brainstorm to come up with as many ideas as possible. Don't evaluate them at this stage. Just write down everything that everyone suggests, no matter how bizarre it may seem at first glance.

2) Go through the list, item by item. Check if they match all the information in the puzzle and the clues. Weigh up the pros and cons of each option. Make a note of points that inspire further discussion or questions. Check the relevance to finding a solution. If you're in doubt, keep the option. You can always discard it later.

3) Test the remaining ideas. Look for loopholes, exceptions, contradictions, or information that would make the solution impossible. Also, look at factors that could make some of the crazier solutions seem more plausible.

4) If the conversation starts to feel repetitive, throw in a random variable. What aspect of the puzzle have you not questioned yet? How would a three-year-old respond?

5) Check your assumptions about each piece of information in the puzzle. Provoke new trains of thought by suggesting that one of these assumptions is false.

6) Evaluate the relevance of each possible solution. Is there a solution that would be viable if the provocative statement was true? Remember the exercise bike?

7) Apply each solution to the problem at hand to assess how effective it would be.

Remember that the aim is to work together as a group. You are trying to find the most solutions to fit each puzzle. The assessment of ideas is based on logic and can be supported or rejected on its merits. Do not take responses personally or become attached to your ideas.

Puzzle 1 - Joe and Bob

Joe finds out that his best friend Bob is sleeping with his wife and plans to discuss it with him over drinks. He buys two identical drinks at the bar and gives one to Bob. Bob dies of poisoning, but Joe is fine even though they finish the same number of drinks. Joe knows that it is because they have different drinking habits. How did the poison get into the drink?

Solutions

1. The poison was in the ice. Bob drank slowly, allowing the poison to melt into his drink. Joe downed his drink quickly before the ice would melt, so he didn't consume any poison.

2. Joe dropped the poison into Bob's drink on his way back to the table.

3. The poison was in the glasses before the drinks were poured. Bob took longer to drink his, so more poison mixed into the drink. Joe downed his drink before enough poison could be absorbed into his drink to have any effect.

4. It was a tropical bar, so drinks had paper umbrellas. Joe dipped the tip of Bob's umbrella in poison, knowing that Bob left the umbrella in until the end.

5. The drinks were martinis. Joe had olives while Bob had a twist of lemon. The poison was on the lemon.

One of these solutions doesn't match up with the information in the original puzzle. Can you spot the error?

Puzzle 2 - Skiing

A newspaper states that Mr. Smith and his wife were skiing in the Alps and that Mrs. Smith had an accident, fell off the mountain, and was killed.

How does the man reading the newspaper know that Mr. Smith murdered his wife?

Solutions

The man reading the paper is the travel agent who sold Mr. Smith his tickets. Smith had bought a round-trip ticket for himself but a one-way ticket for his wife.

The man is a Catholic priest. He'd heard Mr. Smith's confession.

Puzzle 3 - Book

A woman went up to a counter and handed the person behind it a book.

"That will be $5, please."

She was happy with the amount and paid the $5 but left the book behind on purpose. Why would she not take the book after paying?

Solutions

The woman was returning a book to the library. The overdue fine was $5.

The woman was mailing the book to her daughter. It was already wrapped and addressed. She had to hand it in at a counter at the post office. The postage fee was $5.

Puzzle 4 - Cabin

A couple enters a cabin only to find that its occupants are dead. They do not call the police because they know no crime was committed. The couple is unconcerned by what they have found; they were expecting to see some corpses.

Solutions

The couple is on a wreck diving expedition to explore aircraft that crashed into the ocean. The occupants had drowned when their plane was involved in a terrible disaster at sea.

The couple were exterminators for an airline. They were inspecting an airplane to be sure the fumigation had been successful.

Puzzle 5 - Snoring

Steve's wife and kids have been complaining for years about how his snoring is annoying. They never expected it to cause the kind of panic and terror it did today. So, who is Steve, and why would his snoring suddenly cause such a reaction in people who heard it for the first time?

Solutions

Steve is a bus driver. He's fallen asleep while driving at high speed on the highway. His passengers panic when they hear him snoring.

Steve is a pilot of a large passenger aircraft. He has recently had a swine flu vaccine and was experiencing temporary episodes of narcolepsy. He was busy talking to an air traffic controller on a loudspeaker when he unexpectedly fell asleep.

Steve also walks in his sleep. He ended up on a neighbor's porch and scared them with his very loud snoring.

Puzzle 6 - Jump

A woman who lives in a 30-story building decides to jump out of her window. She survives the fall with no injuries. How did that happen?

Solutions

She lives on the first floor of the 30-story building. So, it wasn't a very long drop from the first-floor window to the ground.

She jumped off the roof with abseiling gear on and climbed down the side of the building.

She jumped onto a fire escape and walked down.

The window opened onto a balcony, so the fall was less than two feet.

Puzzle 7 - Bear

A woman spotted a bear in the distance. Instead of being afraid, she ran excitedly toward it. How could she be happy to see a dangerous animal?

Solutions

She was at the zoo.

Her son was the mascot for his high school football team and had to wear a bear cub costume. She was attending one of their games.

She had returned to the playground to find the teddy bear that her toddler had left behind earlier that day.

Puzzle 8 - The Room

Three people enter a room, but only two walk out. The room is empty. Where is the third person?

Solutions

The third person was in a wheelchair and wheeled out.

The room was a sauna. The third person fainted and had to be taken out on a stretcher.

They were a family going to an evening movie. The third person was a child who fell asleep and had to be carried out.

Puzzle 9 - 12 Marbles

Imagine you have 12 marbles and three identical bags. There are three creative ways to place the 12 marbles in the three bags so that each bag contains the same number of marbles.

One way would be to put four marbles in each bag. Can you find the other two ways?

Solutions

Put 12 marbles in each bag -> put the 12 marbles in the first bag, next put the first bag inside the second bag, and then put the second bag inside the third bag. Put 6 marbles in each bag -> put 6 marbles in the first bag, next put 6 marbles in the second bag, and then put the second bag inside the third bag.

CONCLUSION

Lateral thinking can be wonderfully liberating after being confined to vertical thinking throughout our school life. But this makes it easy to go too far off the rails. The types of logical fallacies used to assess arguments in law or philosophy can also be helpful in examining our creative solutions. While it can be effective to build on connections that others may have missed, we also need to be sure that we are not making incorrect assumptions about the original data. This is a list of common fallacies of logic.

So, what are logical fallacies, and how do they affect lateral thinking? There are two major types of arguments that can be proved to be flawed, false, or deceptive. A formal fallacy occurs when we draw conclusions inconsistent with the evidence. Informal fallacies deal more with the context and content of the argument itself. It is essential to assess each step of our lateral thinking processes to ensure that we don't make simple errors in logic. One slight leap to a false conclusion can lead to us being far off target by the time we reach a solution.

Below is a list of fifteen basic logic fallacies discussed at the university level. Of course, they are not all shared in the process of lateral thinking, but it is helpful to be aware of possible flaws in your arguments or solutions.

Ad Hominem

This fallacy happens when an opponent attacks the person instead of the argument. Unfortunately, people sometimes resort to using irrelevant personal characteristics such as physical appearance, ethnic background, or other irrelevant characteristics to discredit the speaker instead of challenging the logic of the argument they are presenting.

Ad hominem attacks are most common in politics, where they are used to influence public opinion about opponents without having to discuss their stance on policy issues.

Personal scandals may not be commonplace in most lateral thinking situations, but we can sometimes make assumptions about situations based on our preconceived ideas about certain characters. It is even possible that we may disregard ideas from specific individuals on our team based on previous experience with them or their job description rather than the strength of their argument.

Straw Man

This type of fallacy stems from the idea of a scarecrow. The scarecrow is in the shape of a person but stuffed with straw. It is merely a distraction to draw attention away from the actual argument. In law, politics, or any other situation of confrontational argument, the purpose would be to intentionally misdirect the audience's attention from a point they cannot challenge to something they can easily defeat. A side effect is often to ridicule their opponent.

In a normal lateral thinking environment, this could include getting stuck in details, not seeing the bigger picture, or following a tangent too far off the tracks.

If we look at our oranges in the basket example again, a straw man argument might be that the extra orange had to come from somewhere. Instead of focusing on how there could be an orange left in the basket, the discussion could get sidetracked into whether somebody else came in afterward and put the seventh orange in the basket.

Appeal to Ignorance

This is quite possibly the silliest logical fallacy there is. It states that something is true or untrue simply because the opposite hasn't been proved yet. Therefore, the argument must be valid because nobody has proved it false is the same logic as the argument must be false because nobody has proved it true.

This can sometimes be useful in creating a provocative statement. But, again, the stationary bicycle example is relevant here. Nobody had proved that it was impossible to cycle ten miles in one spot, so somebody found a way to make it possible.

False Dilemma/False Dichotomy

In this fallacy, the argument focuses on two (usually extreme) aspects of an argument, presenting them as the only alternatives. This is a very effective tool in marketing and politics. The aim is usually to gain support for radical or controversial policies. It is a divide and conquer strategy.

The most recent example is the global reaction to the Covid 19 pandemic and vaccination plans. The population of the entire planet became divided into vaxxers and anti-vaxxers. Both sides are equally passionate and sincere in their arguments against each other. The middle ground could have been to take a bit longer to do more tests and peer reviews to confirm data before rolling out the vaccine.

False dilemmas are usually more of a problem in vertical thinking than in lateral thinking because our focus here is on finding the most options possible.

Slippery Slope

As the name suggests, a slippery slope argument presumes that one step will lead to a controllable course of consequences.

It starts with something simple, and then each consecutive step becomes more far-fetched until the conclusion appears completely ridiculous. There may be a slight connection between the first step and the second, but by the end, there is no evidence at all to support the preposterous claims.

Every generation of teenagers has used this logic (or lack of it) on their parents. "If you force me to go with you, I'll miss the party! If I don't go to the party, everybody will think I'm lame. Nobody will want to be friends with me. I'll never get married, and you'll never have grandchildren."

Slippery slope fallacies can sometimes sneak into lateral thinking exercises when we start thinking about implementing solutions. Be careful to check every step of the process for logic and evidence. Don't jump to conclusions based on assumptions. It is only a fallacy when the conclusions have no logical support. Can you see the difference in the following examples?

Example 1

The school policy is that if a player misses practice, they can't be a starter on game day. So, if you don't go to baseball practice today, you won't be a starter in Saturday's game. Then you won't be the first freshman to start on the varsity baseball team at your school."

Example 2

Missing practice means that you have no discipline. People without discipline do not even graduate high school. You will never get into college or get a decent job. Instead, you are going to end up homeless and sleeping on a park bench.

Circular Argument

This happens when somebody tries to use their assumption to prove their conclusion. They repeat the assumption as if it was a conclusion, without any outside evidence to support it.

This fallacy is one I'm sure you've encountered recently. Many young job seekers are told that they can't be employed because they don't have experience. How are they supposed to get experience if the reason they cannot get experience is because they do not have experience?

Another place we see this often is in religion. How do you know God exists? My Holy Book says so. How do you know your Holy Book is true? Because it's the word of God.

Hasty Generalization

A hasty generalization uses random examples to substantiate claims with no supporting evidence. It is easy to disprove a hasty generalization because something true in one case is probably not true in another. All you have to do to refute it is to find cases where it is not true.

One of the reasons hasty generalizations are common is that the standards for relevant evidence can be flexible based on the claim made and the environment in which it is being made.

Red Herring

We've seen quite a few of these in this book. Red herrings are statements introduced with the specific aim of distraction to draw attention away from the topic towards an irrelevant or false conclusion. The difference between a red herring and a straw man fallacy is relevant to the original topic. A straw man argument challenges a less significant aspect of the same argument, making the objection easier to overcome. A red herring leads you down a completely different tangent.

Appeal to Hypocrisy

This is one of the easiest fallacies to spot. It can only work if one is focused on laying blame or assigning guilt. Instead of arguing the case, the person points out the same or similar behavior in their opponent. The gist is usually, "How can you tell me that what I did is wrong when you did the same thing?"

The argument is neutralized by acknowledging that it has always been the same. "Drunk driving is just as stupid no matter who is doing it. I was lucky I didn't kill someone. You might not be so lucky."

This almost rarely comes up in lateral thinking exercises because there is little room for personal attacks in the situations presented in this book. However, it is useful to understand the mechanism especially when it comes up in your personal life.

Causal Fallacy

These have come up a few times in the crime section of our puzzles. This fallacy assumes that an event that happened first caused an event that happened after, with only circumstantial evidence or sometimes no evidence to prove that a relationship exists between the events.

Lateral thinking often requires seeing unusual connections between events or facts. We need to be especially careful when making assumptions about cause and effect. Even a direct correspondence does not prove a causal relationship. Roosters crowing at sunrise doesn't mean that we would live in perpetual darkness without roosters.

Sunk Cost

The term "sunk cost" in economics refers to expenses that have already been incurred and cannot be recovered. In general usage, it results in people continuing to follow a path because of how much they have already invested in it, without considering whether additional costs would be worth the potential benefits.

This is something to look out for when using lateral thinking in real-life situations. Solutions need to take into account investments that have already been made when weighing up the costs and benefits of a new approach. Look at what is already being done and evaluate whether it is more effective to continue on the existing path, modify what already exists or scratch it all and start again.

Many people choose their college subjects based on high school experience rather than future plans. However, after a year or two of intense study, it becomes difficult to give up that hard work, even if they know that they would be happier in a different field.

Appeal to Authority

This can only be a valid argument when the authority you quote is relevant to the subject of the argument. An expert in a subject can provide useful information to strengthen a claim so it can be presented as valid evidence. It becomes a fallacy when it is misused to support an argument in cases where their expertise or authority is illegitimate, overstated, or irrelevant to the topic. Sometimes the level of expertise of the authority being quoted can be a matter of perception.

Using a formula one driver's opinion about motor mechanics to prove a point is not the same as quoting an engineer.

Equivocation

This is also a fallacy that can be used in brain teasers to test your ability to recognize ambiguity. However, in law, politics, and advertising, equivocation is more often about finding loopholes or deliberately choosing language that manipulates emotions or logic to confuse, deceive, or mislead others.

Many situations can have multiple explanations. It is important to examine as many options as possible when solving problems. Sometimes the least common assumptions can provide the most plausible solutions.

In creative situations such as poetry or humor it can be a pun or a play on words. However, when it is done with malicious intent, it becomes a fallacy.

Appeal to Pity

An appeal to pity relies on provoking your emotions to win an argument rather than factual evidence. Appealing to pity attempts to pull on an audience's heartstrings, distract them, and support their point of view.

Someone accused of a crime using a cane or walker to appear feebler in front of a jury is one example of appeal to pity. The appearance of disability isn't an argument on the case merits, but it's intended to sway the jury's opinion anyway.

Which of these is a fallacious appeal to emotion and which one is not?

EXAMPLE 1

"Professor, you have to give me an A on this paper. I know I only turned in a sentence and some clip art, but you have to understand, my grandmother suddenly died while traveling in the Northern Yukon. Her funeral was there, so I had to travel, and my parents got divorced in the middle of the ceremony, and all the stress caused me to become catatonic for two weeks. So have some pity — my grandmother's last wish was that I would get an A in this class."

EXAMPLE 2

"Professor, I know this work was subpar, and I feel pretty bad about it. I'd like to schedule a meeting with you to discuss how I can do better on our next assignment."

Bandwagon Fallacy

The bandwagon fallacy assumes something is true (or right or good) because others agree with it. In other words, the fallacy argues that if everyone thinks a certain way, then you should, too.

One problem with this kind of reasoning is that the broad acceptance of a claim or action doesn't mean that it's factually justified. Moreover, people can be mistaken, confused, deceived, or even irrationally passionate in their opinions, so using them to make an argument is flawed.

It is an interesting balancing act to be able to think out of the box without falling into the traps of logical fallacies. Look through the list of fallacies again and think about which puzzles come to mind when you read each description.

We have repeatedly emphasized that the point of this book is not about being right or wrong. You were taught how to think in a system designed for the Industrial Age. Times changed, and the requirements of the workplace evolved. Creativity and problem-solving skills are now essential criteria for most employment options.

It is now more important than ever to objectively understand how your mind works. The way you think is not cast in stone. Thinking is a skill that can be learned like any other. Look at how your thought patterns evolved through the series of puzzles in this book. What fallacies are you most likely to believe or commit in your thought processes?

Become aware of how you think instead of what you think. It will change your understanding of the world and your place in it.

REFERENCES

A quote by Bob Ross. (n.d.). Www.goodreads.com. https://www.goodreads.com/quotes/10320-we-don-t-make-mistakes-just-happy-little-accidents

Abigail, T. S. (2018, August 7). *How Lateral Thinking Just Might Save Your Business*. Toggl Blog. https://toggl.com/blog/lateral-thinking-save-your-business

Bellis, M. (2019, November 17). *How Much Do You Know About the History and Invention of WD-40?* ThoughtCo. https://www.thoughtco.com/wd-40-1992659#:~:text=WD%2D40%20was%20invented%20by

Edward De Bono. (1971). *New think : the use of lateral thinking in the generation of new ideas*. Basic Books.

Edward de Bono Quotes. (n.d.). BrainyQuote. Retrieved March 2, 2022, from https://www.brainyquote.com/quotes/edward_de_bono_389925

How to Harness the Power of Lateral Thinking to Enhance Creativity? (2020, April 20). Awfis. https://www.awfis.com/inspiration/how-to-harness-the-power-of-lateral-thinking-to-enhance-creativity

Mann, S. B. (2019, April 10). *100 Brain Teasers With Answers for Kids and Adults*. IcebreakerIdeas. https://icebreakerideas.com/brain-teasers/

Mann, S. B. (2020, August 26). *31 Tricky Lateral Thinking Puzzles (with Answers)*. IcebreakerIdeas. https://icebreakerideas.com/lateral-thinking-puzzles/

Muxworthy, M. (2018, January 29). *Top 70 lateral thinking puzzles. Extra answers. Clever clues*. Michael Muxworthy - Lateral Thinking Author of Fiction. https://michaelmuxworthy.com/lateral-thinking-puzzles/

Post-it Note. (2022, January 18). Wikipedia. https://en.wikipedia.org/wiki/Post-it_Note#:~:text=In%201968%2C%20Dr.

Provocation and Movement. (n.d.). Www.diegm.uniud.it. Retrieved February 10, 2022, from http://www.diegm.uniud.it/create/Handbook/techniques/List/ProvAndMov.php

Ramkrishnan, P., & Dhanavel, S. P. (2018). *Developing Oral Communication Skills of Architecture Students through De Bono's Lateral Thinking Tool Redesign*.

src="https://www.rd.com/wp-content/uploads/2021/04/80345Phillips-e1617390378164.jpg?fit=50, img class="avatar" alt="Hedy P., Jul. 15, 50" width="50" height="50">Hedy

P., & 2021. (2021, July 15). *20 Challenging Lateral Thinking Puzzles That Are Harder Than They Seem.* Reader's Digest. https://www.rd.com/article/lateral-thinking-puzzles/

Tandon, R. (2015, December 8). *Entrepreneurs: "Don't sell the steak, sell the sizzle" and other Wheelerisms.* Www.linkedin.com. https://www.linkedin.com/pulse/entrepreneurs-dont-sell-steak-sizzle-other-rajiv-tandon-ph-d-/

Thinking outside the Box Managing Successful Innovations Unit 11: Lateral Thinking and Creativity. (n.d.). Retrieved March 2, 2022, from http://www.study365.co.uk/wp-content/uploads/2017/12/Unit-11-Lateral-Thinking-and-Creativity.pdf

Thompson, E. (2021, September 21). *15 Logical Fallacies You Should Know Before Getting Into a Debate.* TheBestSchools.org; thebestschools.org. https://thebestschools.org/magazine/15-logical-fallacies-know/

Image References

(n.d.-a). https://pixabay.com/get/ge349554d5de1e9d158753639dfbeefddf797d87d0e3153c3613004a537a897665bb15a341a06257b45c9fa9e15f2de56_640.jpg

(n.d.-b). https://pixabay.com/get/g91208996fb6c2368a1a77540a6c5574a29cbb4076d5f4c043bab5c32da07b222119e684ae9aa191941dfad025895a845_640.jpg

(n.d.-c). https://pixabay.com/get/gdf8e68a282920e50a8c810d3737bea04c46508732524ec188aa851f9d7e5fcabfae44389540ed7c86d974b2357607a63_640.jpg

(n.d.-d). https://pixabay.com/get/gae137ba0310ad49df4b5e4fe5047bc8071acb29987965d2d1c148adf2382313f0c95a1e6466c06b46b20f9b2c7914c74_640.jpg

(n.d.-e). https://pixabay.com/get/g79ac8c23cac3ff7bb9f12814379bae19ea9f50bbddb7f44d1aa179c500ad0f40013af07cf4bf3c52c6c35c9a3fabc8cd_640.jpg

(n.d.-f). https://pixabay.com/get/g94db40b01fe7f1534739a1375fbb38113036e58da44b4fc57dba7a1e9bad9926b692401ece348dc36dd0cfb792962712_640.jpg

(n.d.-g). https://pixabay.com/get/gf90e9cec0171bf1b889e7b1161602c70ca7c82c81d1b56a6424aabf1dee462e03137186dd3d85ac468983caccf0bf978_640.jpg

(n.d.-h). https://pixabay.com/get/ga3f922c8da6ee643fb5ead0dd5c46ae2593786db314b2417d267151c73e7504fb0d55e4ad635869db46a6c0652c732c3_640.jpg

(n.d.-i). https://pixabay.com/get/g646ab38454a1ca10ebbb13e78c5c3e4408a6d4f9de693a92d32d11f3106439ab6655d32f74e965c6582260f98a4e3835_640.jpg

(n.d.-j). https://pixabay.com/get/g90b31343e29bd953691f179d8d39403e0829e2b813f57621a338871d67a9244424a4dacbe8fb1d5d30a42c84a390a223_640.jpg

Visit Us Online

https://pantheria.store

a Find our Books on Amazon

▶ Pantheria

📷 @Pantheria.lofi

f @Pantheria.lofi

Made in the USA
Columbia, SC
14 February 2023

11934063R00063